Assessment Tests in
English
for Key Stage 2

Peter Smith

Nelson

Thomas Nelson and Sons Ltd
Nelson House Mayfield Road
Walton-on-Thames Surrey
KT12 5PL UK

Thomas Nelson Australia
102 Dodds Street
South Melbourne
Victoria 3205 Australia

Nelson Canada
1120 Birchmount Road
Scarborough Ontario
M1K 5G4 Canada

First Published by Thomas Nelson and Sons Ltd 1993
This edition published 1995

I⟨T⟩P Thomas Nelson is an International Thomson
Publishing Company

I⟨T⟩P is used under licence

ISBN 0-17-420269-5

NPN 9 8 7 6 5 4 3

Printed in China

Acknowledgements

The author and publisher acknowledge the use of
following copyright material:

Extracts from *Living Legends* by Anna McLeay;
'Birthday' and 'The Ghost's Song' by Verna Kilburn from
the Open Door series: **adaptations:** information about
cows based on *Cows on the Farm* by Tessa Potter and
Donna Bailey; 'Roman Roads' based on 'All roads lead
to Rome' from *Watch This Space* Book 3 by Steve Berry;
all published by Thomas Nelson and Sons Limited.

To parents

National Curriculum Tests

The work your child studies in school is set out in the National Curriculum. This tells teachers what children should be learning at the different stages of their development throughout their school life. The first part of the curriculum, for the infant years up to age 7, is called Key Stage 1. Children then study Key Stage 2 from age 7 to 11. The subjects they study contain work at different levels of ability and schools monitor pupils' progress continuously. At the ages of 7 and 11, children take National Tests to help their teachers confirm which level of attainment they have reached. Children start school working towards level 1 and most of them should reach level 2 by the age of 7, and level 4 when they are 11.

How this book can help your child

This book is to give your child some practice in doing tests at home. Working through the exercises will help your child to see that tests are not frightening and that it can be fun to find out how much you know about a subject. The exercises will:

- Give your child practice in the security of a home environment and help him or her to feel comfortable about taking the tests
- Enable you to estimate the level at which your child is working
- Provide many examples of the kinds of questions that could be set in the tests. Although they are not actual National Tests, the exercises are arranged at the various levels described in the National Curriculum.

How can you help

Most of the tests are self-explanatory and once you have made sure your child understands what to do, encourage him or her to do the test quietly without help as far as possible. Each test will probably take about 30 to 40 minutes.

- Mark the tests with the help of the answers at the back of the book as soon as possible after they are completed.
- It may be useful and encouraging to your child to start off with the early tests in the book, even if you are sure he or she is working at higher levels.
- Praise success and if difficulties arise encourage your child to leave the work for a while. Above all, make the tests as enjoyable as possible.

English at Key Stage 2

Many aspects of English are covered in these tests including reading, writing, grammar and the use of words. Assessment in some aspects may inevitably be subjective. This is particularly so when children are required to write their own ideas or when they are asked to think of alternative vocabulary. An exercise book should be available for those occasions when more space is needed or your child wants to make a second attempt. Encourage your child to make appropriate use of a dictionary and thesaurus.

CONTENTS

The Alphabet and Spelling

a b c d e f g h i j k l m n o p q r s t u v w x y z

A Answer these questions:

1. How many letters are there in the alphabet? _____

2. Which letter comes after 'c'? _____

3. Which letter comes after 'y'? _____

4. Which letter comes before 'v'? _____

5. Which letter comes before 'k'? _____

6. Which is the first letter of ? _____

7. Which is the first letter of ? _____

8. Which is the first letter of ? _____

9. Which is the first letter of ? _____

10. Which is the first letter of ? _____

B

1. Read through this list of short words which are in alphabetical order:

ant   bed   cat   dog   egg   fan   get   hat   ink   jam   key   leg   mud
nut   old   pin   quiz   red   sit   tap   use   vain   web   X-ray   yam   zip

Now write another list choosing a different short word for each letter.

_____

_____

_____

_____

2. Now put these words in alphabetical order.
You will have to think about second letter order in some cases.

purple   yellow   black   violet   green   brown   red   white   pink

_____

_____

C Nouns are naming words. Rewrite these nouns in alphabetical order:

lorry bus tractor aeroplane van helicopter car jeep motorcycle fire-engine

_____

_____

_____

D SPELLING (letter strings)
Sometimes you know which string of letters to write because you hear their sound in
a word. Read through the sentences below and underline the two words with the
same letter string. Try to find at least three more examples. Number 1 is done for you.

1. The <u>king</u> wore an enormous ruby <u>ring</u>.   sing   thing   wing

2. The cat fell down the well.   _____

3. He kicked the ball over the wall.   _____

4. The windmill was up on the hill.   _____

5. She had a hole in the sole of her shoe.   _____

6. I will hide inside this cupboard.   _____

7. A duck was stuck in the mud.   _____

8. We need more flour to bake a cake.   _____

9. We climbed the stile and walked for a mile.   _____

10. I knew the time because I heard the clock chime.   _____

E Read these ten sentence endings and write each one beside the sentence beginning it matches.

- bandaged my grazed knee.
- made the audience laugh.
- marked all my sums right.
- was barking by the gate.
- loves a saucer of milk to drink.
- has gone wrong so we cannot watch it.
- zoomed noisily over the house.
- are good at painting.
- is chicken and chips.
- swam round and round its bowl.

1. The lost dog _____

2. The aeroplane _____

3. The kind nurse _____

4. The goldfish _____

5. My teacher _____

6. The children in our class _____

7. A funny clown _____

8. My favourite dinner _____

9. Our cat _____

10. Our television set _____

Sentences

A Read this information about cows.

Farmers keep cows for their milk. The cows are milked twice a day when their udders are full. In summer cows are kept out in fields. They eat lots of grass. In winter they are taken into a cowshed. The farmer has to feed them with hay. The cowshed must be kept clean. Cows are given clean straw to lie on. When the straw is dirty, it is removed. The farmer brings fresh straw in its place.

The information about cows is written in sentences.

1.   How many words are there in the first sentence? _____

2.   Copy out the tenth word in the second sentence. _____

3.   How many sentences are there? _____

4.   Copy out the third sentence. _____

     _____

5.   Copy out the eighth sentence. _____

     _____

6.   Copy out the last word of the seventh sentence. _____

B Write sentences to answer these questions.

1.   Why do farmers keep cows?

     _____

2.   How often are cows milked?

     _____

3.   When do farmers milk cows?

     _____

4. Where are cows kept in the summer?

   _____

5. What do cows eat in the summer?

   _____

6. Where are cows kept in the winter?

   _____

7. What do cows eat in the winter?

   _____

8. What do cows lie on?

   _____

9. What is the name for a baby cow?

   _____

10. Name two other farm animals.

   _____

C   Rewrite the information below about a calf, putting in all necessary capital letters and full stops.

a baby cow is called a calf a newborn calf lies on the grass beside its mother the cow licks her calf to clean it when the calf tries to stand, its legs are wobbly the calf soon gets hungry it drinks warm milk from its mother

_____

_____

_____

_____

_____

D　Using words in sentences.

Tom and Kim had to use the word <u>stung</u> in a sentence and this is what they wrote.

Tom:　I got stung.

Kim:　When I am in the country I watch out for nettles because I don't like
being stung.

Kim's sentence is much more interesting than Tom's.
Use each of the words below in an interesting sentence.

1.　duck _____

_____

2.　circus _____

_____

3.　snail _____

_____

4.　earth _____

_____

5.　weather _____

_____

6.　colour _____

_____

7.　rustle _____

_____

8.　muscle _____

_____

Birthday

My birthday is coming and I know what I'd like.
I don't want a football or a whistle or a bike.
I don't ask for much, Mum, and I won't nag.
I just want a Mini – a Sierra – or a Jag!

No. I don't mean a toy, Mum. I mean one that's real.
An engine! A motor! A fast set of wheels.
I'd buy the petrol if you'd get me a car,
I'd drive very slowly and I wouldn't go far.

Now don't start shouting, Mum. Don't make a fuss.
I don't want a lorry or a tractor or a bus.
Just a little motor car. It needn't be new.
I'm sure that you'll agree with me when you've thought it through.

What are you saying, Mum? You've got to be *how old*?
And what's a driving licence, Mum? Well, I was never told.
It seemed a good idea, Mum, but I will use my brain –
Now I've had a little think, Mum. What about a plane?

Verna Kilburn

A   Answer each question with a sentence:

1. How many verses are there?

   _____

2. How many lines in each verse?

   _____

3. Who is talking in the poem?

_____

4. Who is being spoken to?

_____

5. What is a driving licence?

_____

_____

6. In the poem there are seven things not being asked for. List them:

_____

_____

B There are two pairs of rhyming words in each verse. Try to find more examples.
Verse 1a has been done for you.

1. verse   1a _____ like   bike _____   _____ hike   pike _____

         1b _____   _____

   verse   2a _____   _____

         2b _____   _____

   verse   3a _____   _____

         3b _____   _____

   verse   4a _____   _____

         4b _____   _____

C CONTRACTIONS

In several places in the poem, an apostrophe is used in place of letters that have been omitted. For example: **I'd** is short for **I would** and the apostrophe is in place of the letters 'woul'. Complete this list:

1. I'd is short for   I would _____

2. don't is short for   _____

3. that's is short for   _____

4. you'd is short for   _____

5. wouldn't is short for _____

6. needn't is short for _____

7. I'm is short for   _____

8. you'll is short for   _____

9. you've is short for   _____

10. what's is short for _____

11. I've is short for   _____

D Write the contractions for the following:

1. cannot   _____

2. does not   _____

3. he is   _____

4. I am   _____

5. that is   _____

6. we will   _____

7. you are   _____

8. they have _____

9. should not _____

E   Rearrange the following to make the first two verses of a poem called *The Ghost's Song* by Verna Kilburn. There are four lines in each verse.

I'm a terrifying ghost, and I'll scare you
for certain. I'm a cross between a monster
and an old net curtain. I can walk
through a wall, I can imitate a bat, I can
turn myself bright purple, and then
horrify the cat.

_____

_____

_____

_____

_____

_____

_____

_____

A legend is a story which has been handed down through the ages and is often thought to be historical, although there is no evidence.

The Legend of Daura

A long time ago in the town of Daura in Northern Nigeria, the people had a <u>serious</u> problem. Daura was a hot, dry place with but one well in which a <u>big</u> snake lived. This snake would only permit water to be drawn on one day a week and so the people often went thirsty.

One day, a prince from another land far across the desert arrived in Daura. He was hot and weary so asked for water. The people told him they had none and explained why. The prince was brave as well as thirsty so he picked up a bucket and strode to the well. The noise woke the snake who reared up from the ledge where he had been sleeping and threatened the prince. The snake expected the prince to run away as the <u>cowardly</u> townsfolk always did but the <u>brave</u> prince . . .

A

1.   What sort of place was Daura?

_____

_____

2.   What does permit mean (as used in the third sentence)?

_____

16

3. What was the serious problem?

_____

_____

_____

4. What sort of prince came from another land?

_____

5. What woke the snake?

_____

6. How do you think the snake threatened the prince?

_____

7. Finish the last sentence.

_____

8. Write a short paragraph to end the story.

_____

_____

_____

_____

_____

_____

_____

_____

_____

_____

B   Adjectives are describing words.
Look at the four words underlined in the legend: <u>serious</u>, <u>big</u>, <u>cowardly</u> and <u>brave</u>.
These four words describe: the problem, the snake, the townsfolk and the prince.

large, valiant, fearful, frightened, grave, huge, courageous gigantic, depressing, daring, timid, scared, earnest, bold, alarming, enormous, fearless, worrying, colossal, nervous.

For **each** underlined word, choose from the box above **five** more words which mean almost the same. Write them in columns.

1. <u>serious</u>   **2.** <u>big</u>   **3.** <u>cowardly</u>   **4.** <u>brave</u>

_____   _____   _____   _____

_____   _____   _____   _____

_____   _____   _____   _____

_____   _____   _____   _____

_____   _____   _____   _____

C   Synonyms are words with similar meanings.
Underline the two words in each line which are synonyms.

1.   terror   brave   lost   fear

2.   pretty   broad   straight   wide

3.   enormous   gigantic   slippery   good

4.   train   halt   stop   policeman

5.   antique   valuable   new   modern

6.   silly   feeble   ugly   weak

7.   foe   friend   neighbour   enemy

8.   moon   rain   dusk   twilight

9.   round   old   puny   circular

10.   astonish   act   surprise   avoid

The Fox And The Stork

A fable by Aesop

D Read this draft of the fable and write your corrected version in the space below. Remember to check the capital letters, full stops and spelling.

a fox invited a stork too dinner, but all he provided wore large flat dishes of soop the fox lapped his up eesily butt the stork with her longe bill cood not get any. The sly fox larfed cruelly at her misfortune.

So, a fue days latter, the stalk returned thee invitation. She servd a tall narro jug of food fo eash of them. Wiv her longe thin nek and bill she could reach write to the botom of her jug the fox, however, wet hungry becos he could not reach the food in his jug it served him right for playin a trick on the stork

_____

_____

_____

_____

_____

_____

_____

_____

_____

_____

_____

_____

_____

_____

The First Piece of Paper

A   These ten sentences about the making of the first sheet of paper are out of order. Read through them carefully.

- He beat the ingredients with a wooden mallet.

- He left it to dry in the sun.

- He put bits of rag, bark, straw, plant stems and old fishing nets in a stone bowl.

- Long ago in China there lived a man named Ts'ai Lun.

- When it was dry, he found he could write on it.

- Ts'ai Lun made a sieve to lift out the pulp mat.

- That was how the first piece of paper was made.

- Then he added water and beat the mixture to a pulp.

- Ts'ai Lun found out how to make paper.

- He noticed that the wet bits stuck together and spread out so they floated on the water like a mat.

Now rearrange the sentences in the correct sequence and write them below.
(Two have already been done for you.)

It would be a good idea to do this on rough paper first.

1. _____

_____

2. Ts'ai Lun found out how to make paper. _____

_____

3. _____

_____

4. He beat the ingredients with a wooden mallet. _____

_____

5. _____

_____

6. _____

_____

7. _____

_____

8. _____

_____

9. _____

_____

10. _____

_____

B   The facts about Ts'ai Lun's paper came from a book. We do get a lot of information from books but we can also learn by asking questions.
Here are some questions for you to answer in sentences. (Notice the ?)

1.   How many children are there in your class at school?

_____

2.   What is your favourite lesson?

_____

3.   What was the title of the last book you read in school?

_____

4.   How many people live in your house?

_____

5.   What foods do you enjoy most?

_____

6.   Are there any foods you don't like at all?

_____

7.   Which of your toys or games do you play with most?

_____

8.   If you could choose, which pet would you like to have?

_____

9.   What is the longest journey you have ever made?

_____

10.   What kind of weather do you like best?

_____

C   Here are some answers to questions.
Write the questions that would get these answers.

1.   I usually go to bed at about half past eight.

   _____

2.   My father is a bus driver and my mother is a doctor.

   _____

3.   I have two brothers but no sisters.

   _____

4.   I like cartoons and programmes about pop music.

   _____

5.   I would like to live in the country.

   _____

6.   On Saturdays I tidy my room before I go out to play.

   _____

7.   I go to the dentist's twice a year unless I have a problem.

   _____

D   DICTATION   Ask an adult to read the sentence from the answer section.

_____

_____

_____

_____

_____

_____

The Letter

Ocean View,
Marine Drive,
SANDY BEACHES,
Devon.

7th May 1993

Dear Sally and Ben,

It <u>seems</u> a long time since we last <u>saw</u> you. We <u>settled</u> down quickly in our new bungalow and <u>like</u> it here.

Your uncle and I invite you both to stay with us for a week of your summer holiday. Sandy Beaches is a lovely place for a holiday. The beaches are superb and there is a new swimming pool. We also have a pier where you can fish.

We hope you accept. Please write and tell us what sort of things you enjoy on holiday so that we can make plans.

Give our love to your mum and dad.

Lots of love,

Auntie Pam

A   Verbs are doing words.
In the first paragraph of Auntie Pam's letter the four verbs are underlined:
<u>seems</u>, <u>saw</u>, <u>settled</u> and <u>like</u>.

1.   Underline all the other verbs in the letter.
2.   How many verbs are underlined altogether? _____

B Past tenses of verbs.
Two of the four verbs in the first paragraph are past tense — saw and settled. **Saw** is the past tense of the verb **to see** and **settled** is the past tense of the verb **to settle**. What are the past tenses of the following verbs (none end in 'ed')?

1. to begin _____

2. to eat _____

3. to leave _____

4. to blow _____

5. to dig _____

6. to fly _____

7. to give _____

8. to know _____

9. to be _____

10. to build _____

11. to fall _____

12. to meet _____

13. to go _____

14. to lose _____

15. to hear _____

16. to catch _____

17. to pay _____

18. to ride _____

19. to sell _____

20. to sing _____

C DICTATION   Ask an adult to read the sentences from the answer section.

_____

_____

_____

_____

_____

_____

_____

_____

_____

D   Imagine that you are Sally or Ben and write a reply to Auntie Pam's letter.
It would be a good idea to start by drafting your reply on rough paper. (Drafting means getting your ideas down quickly without worrying too much about neatness and correctness.) Then revise your draft (look through it and make changes to improve it). Don't forget to tell Auntie Pam what you would enjoy doing on holiday. Next, edit your letter (check spelling, punctuation, etc.). Finally, write your letter carefully below. Remember to set it out like Auntie Pam's.

_____

_____

_____

_____

_____

_____

_____

_____

_____

_____

_____

_____

_____

_____

_____

_____

_____

Ants

Ants <u>reside</u> in large groups called colonies. The most important ant is the queen. She lays the eggs. There are also soldier ants who <u>guard</u> the nest and <u>hordes</u> of worker ants who <u>construct</u> the nest, <u>gather</u> food and rear the young.

Ants eat several <u>types</u> of food including caterpillars, leaves and fungi. They also eat seeds and they particularly <u>enjoy</u> sweet things. Ants even keep greenfly in the same way that humans keep cows. Ants get honeydew from greenfly.

Although ants cannot talk, they can communicate. They <u>transmit</u> messages by smells. Some smells say 'here is food' while other smells ask for <u>help</u> to carry something. Ants can also tell the difference between friend and <u>foe</u> by their smells.

A   Think of another word for each of the underlined words. You may use a dictionary or thesaurus if you wish.

1.   reside   _____
2.   guard   _____
3.   hordes   _____
4.   construct   _____
5.   gather   _____

6.   types   _____
7.   enjoy   _____
8.   transmit   _____
9.   help   _____
10.   foe   _____

B   List five foods ants like to eat:

_____

_____

_____

_____

_____

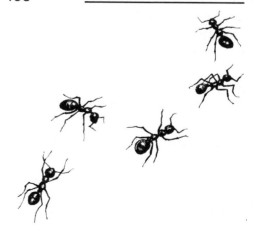

C   Give three examples of how ants use their sense of smell.
Write a sentence for each example.

1. _____

2. _____

3. _____

D   Is honeydew   •   honey mixed with dew?
                •   a fluid obtained from greenfly?
                •   the juice of sugar cane?

Honeydew is _____

E

Honeybees

Honeybees also live in large colonies. Left to themselves, they make nests in trees, roofs or rocks but beekeepers make hives for them. The queen bee lays more than a thousand eggs a day. Worker bees work hard looking after the babies, searching for food and cleaning and protecting the nest.

Worker bees collect pollen and nectar from flowers. They eat some and bring the remainder back to the nest. There they feed the babies and other bees before storing the rest in cells in the wax combs they make. Nectar is turned into honey before it is stored.

Bees have an interesting method of communicating. When a bee finds nectar, it returns to the nest and does a little dance.

List four jobs done by worker bees.

1. _____

2. _____

3. _____

4. _____

F   Differences and similarities.

The information about ants and bees is arranged in three paragraphs:

- How they live.
- What they eat.
- How they communicate.

Enter information on this chart to show the ways in which they are similar and the ways in which they are different.

	ANTS	BEES
How they live (SIMILAR)	1. _____ 2. _____ 3. _____ 4. _____ 5. _____ 6. _____	
What they eat (DIFFERENT)	_____ _____ _____	_____ _____ _____
How they keep food (DIFFERENT)	_____ _____ _____	_____ _____ _____
How they communicate (DIFFERENT)		

From the Legend of King Arthur

King Arthur was worried because he had no sword. "Come with me," Merlin said. "I will take you to one." Merlin led Arthur to a wide lake. At the centre of the lake was an arm reaching up out of the water. Its hand held up a sword encased in a sheath.

"Look," said Merlin. "That is the sword I spoke of and here comes the Lady of the Lake. Speak <u>courteously</u> to her and she will give you the sword."

"Fair Lady," Arthur asked the Lady of the Lake, "what sword is this? I wish to have it because I no longer have one of my own."

"The sword is mine," said the Lady. "You may have it, if you will give me a gift when I ask for it."

Arthur agreed and the Lady <u>indicated</u> a boat he could use. He rowed across the lake and <u>grasped</u> the sword by the handle. The arm slowly <u>submerged</u> into the water. When Arthur got back to the shore, Merlin told him, "Your sword is called Excalibur. Keep it close to you as long as you live."

"The <u>sheath</u> is far more valuable than the sword," said Merlin. "While you wear it, you will lose no blood, even if you are badly <u>wounded</u>."

From that day on, Arthur felt more capable of fighting against his enemies and won many famous victories.

A   Answer these questions:

1.   Who took King Arthur to the lake? _____

2.   What was Excalibur? _____

3.   Who did Excalibur belong to? _____

Answer these questions in sentences:

4.   Why was the sheath more valuable than the sword?

_____

_____

_____

5.   What happened to the arm when Arthur took the sword?

_____

_____

_____

6.   How do we know that Excalibur made Arthur more confident about dealing with his enemies?

_____

_____

_____

B   What is the meaning of these words from the story?
You may use a dictionary if you wish.

1.   courteously _____

2.   indicated _____

3.   grasped _____

4. submerged _____

5. sheath _____

6. wounded _____

C   In the story there is a great deal of speaking. When speech is written down, the words spoken are enclosed by speech marks ''. . .''.

How many sets of speech marks occur in the story? _____

D   The story is continued below but without capital letters and full stops, etc. Write it out with correct punctuation:

arthur thought it was time he got married he summoned merlin and said i want to marry a princess called guinevere merlin was a wizard and knew it was not a good idea he advised arthur not to marry guinevere arthur said i want no one but guinevere for my wife so go and arrange the wedding

_____

_____

_____

_____

_____

_____

_____

_____

_____

_____

_____

E

Pronouns are words that take the place of nouns.
Read through this story about Anne.

Anne left <u>Anne's</u> house late so <u>Anne</u> ran as fast as <u>Anne</u> could to catch the bus. The bus was early, but <u>Anne</u> still caught <u>the bus</u> because the driver waited for <u>Anne</u>. Anne was grateful to the driver so <u>Anne</u> thanked <u>the driver</u>.

Some words are repeated unnecessarily. These words are underlined. Write out the story using one of the pronouns **her, him, it** *or* **she** *in place of the underlined words.*

Anne left _____ house late so _____ ran as fast as _____ could to catch the

bus. The bus was early but _____ still caught _____ because the driver waited

for _____ . Anne was grateful to the driver so _____ thanked _____ .

F

Underline the correct pronoun in the brackets.

1. Tom and (me I) played football in the park.

2. Suzie shared her sweets with (me I).

3. The ship's captain ordered (he him) to send the signal.

4. (She Her) gave (I me) a new book.

5. A huge dog chased (she her) but (she her) got away.

6. (Us We) invited (they them) to our party.

7. Let (me I) know when (they them) are coming.

8. (His He) car was very fast so (he him) overtook (us we).

G PREFIXES AND SUFFIXES

Look at the words **submerged** and **famous** in the legend.
Submerged begins with the prefix <u>sub</u> which means 'under'.
Famous ends with the suffix <u>ous</u> which means 'full of'.

Many opposites are formed by adding the prefix <u>dis</u> or <u>un</u>.
Write the opposites of these words using the correct prefix (dis or un).

1. agree _____

2. certain _____

3. comfortable _____

4. employed _____

5. like _____

6. mount _____

7. equal _____

8. honest _____

9. even _____

10. expected _____

11. advantage _____

12. dress _____

13. fair _____

14. respect _____

15. loyal _____

16. wary _____

17. appear _____

18. fortunate _____

19. appoint _____

20. believe _____

21. allow _____

22. wrap _____

23. usual _____

24. obey _____

25. healthy _____

26. tidy _____

27. pack _____

28. approve _____

29. happy _____

30. qualify _____

31. known _____

32. trust _____

H   Here are some more words which have prefixes:

> illegal   incomplete   interval   postpone
> prepare   rewrite   submarine   subway

Match each word in the box to the correct definition.

1.   a tunnel under a road for safe crossing _____

2.   the time between two halves of a programme _____

3.   put something off till later _____

4.   a boat that operates under the sea _____

5.   not all the pieces are there _____

6.   get ready to do something _____

7.   not allowed by law _____

8.   write it again more carefully _____

I   Here are some more words which have suffixes:

> careless   famous   comfortable   gosling
> lovable   princess   waitress   wonderful

Match each word in the box to the correct definition.

1.   easy to like _____

2.   very well known _____

3.   not paying enough attention to what you're doing _____

4.   a lady who serves in a restaurant _____

5.   the wife of a prince _____

6.   relaxed and at ease _____

7.   a baby goose _____

8.   surprisingly good _____

35

Power

The first people on earth had only the <u>power</u> of their own muscles to do work and to move things. Then they began to use large animals to do work that they were not strong enough to do for themselves. Hence the well-known saying — "He was as strong as an ox."

Later, people learned how to make simple machines and to use animals, the wind and moving water to work them. Then, later still, came the invention of the steam engine in which heated water was turned into steam and the pressure of the steam created power to work machinery. At first wood, which was easily <u>available</u> in the many forests which covered the land, was used to boil the water and make steam. Then coal and oil were <u>located</u> under the ground by geologists.

Nowadays, most machinery is powered by electricity which is generally <u>produced</u> in power stations. Fuel such as coal, oil, gas and uranium are used to heat water and raise steam. The steam drives the generators which generate electricity. Some electricity is also produced using the forces of wind and water. These are renewable resources and, as fossil fuels will <u>eventually</u> be exhausted, we hope that, in future, an even greater <u>proportion</u> of our electricity may be generated that way.

A Answer these questions in sentences:

1. How does a steam engine work?

_____

_____

2. Where is electricity produced?

_____

3. Why is wood a renewable resource?

_____

_____

4. What is a geologist?

_____

_____

B Find a synonym for each word below, as used in the passage.

1. power   _____

2. available   _____

3. located   _____

4. produced   _____

5. eventually   _____

6. proportion   _____

C

1. In the passage opposite, there are four clear stages of power development. As a summary, write the four stages in the boxes below.

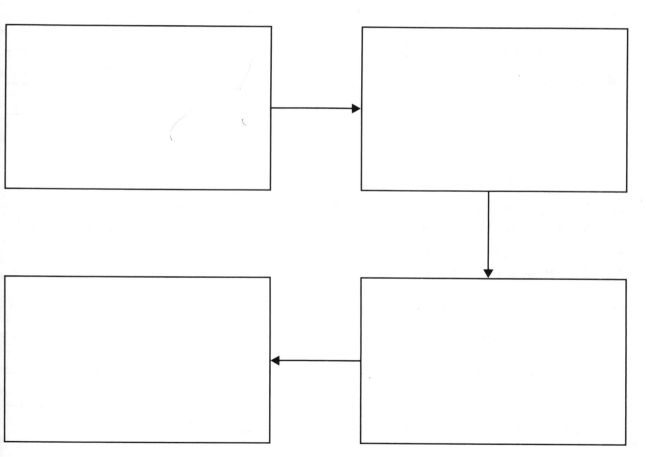

2. List five things in your house which use electricity.

_____

_____

D   SIMILES

In the first paragraph of *Power* we read: 'as strong as an ox'.
This compares a man with an ox and is a figure of speech called a simile.
Write in the words to complete the similes below.

1. as sly as a _____

2. as slow as a _____

3. as brave as a_____

4. as proud as a_____

5. as busy as a _____

6. as blind as a _____

7. as fat as a _____

8. as wise as an _____

9. as stubborn as a_____

10. as brown as a _____

11. as white as _____

12. as fresh as a _____

13. as green as _____

14. as cold as _____

E   Commas indicate a brief pause. Commas are used to separate items in a list except the last two where we use 'and'. In the piece on *Power* we find two examples:

- animals, the wind and moving water
- coal, oil, gas and uranium

Write out these lists properly punctuated:

1. For tea we had sandwiches cakes biscuits ice cream

_____

_____

2. On the farm we saw hens sheep cows pigs horses

_____

_____

3. At school we did sums reading writing

_____

4. I like reading books about travel sport giants

_____

5. At the shop we bought tea sugar rice bread butter

_____

6. We went fishing and caught herring cod

_____

7. My friends live in the same road at numbers 8 15 19 20

_____

_____

8. For my birthday I had a new bike a computer game an annual

_____

_____

9. I have three brothers one sister two aunts three uncles

_____

_____

F DICTATION   Ask an adult to read the sentences from the answer section.

_____

_____

_____

_____

_____

_____

_____

_____

The Legend of the Glastonbury Thorn

from *Living Legends* by Anna McLeay

In England at the town of Glastonbury, in Somerset, it is still possible to see the descendants of the Glastonbury Thorn, a hawthorn of mysterious origin. Glastonbury itself is connected closely with the legend of King Arthur and the Knights of the Round Table.

Legend tells how the Holy Grail was brought to Britain by Joseph of Arimathea. He was a rich man written about in the Bible, who lent his tomb to the disciples for the burial of Jesus. When he landed at Glastonbury he drove his staff into the ground. Miraculously, it came to life, and blossomed, growing into a hawthorn tree. This famous thorn is supposed to be found in front of the Parish Church of St John the Baptist, in Glastonbury, and some of its blossom is sent to the Royal Family every year. In 1752 the British calendar was altered, and the date of Christmas Eve was moved. The trees, however, have never changed, they still bloom every year in early January, about the same date as the old Christmas Eve.

A   Answer these questions in sentences.

1.   What is a legend? (See Test 4.)

_____

_____

_____

2.   What was the Glastonbury Thorn?

_____

_____

3. How did the first one come to be planted?

_____

_____

4. What do we know about Joseph of Arimathea?

_____

_____

5. Where in Glastonbury is the famous thorn supposed to be found?

_____

_____

6. What still happens annually?

_____

_____

7. On which special day did the tree blossom originally?

_____

_____

8. It no longer blooms on that day. Why not?

_____

_____

9. In which county can you see the famous thorn?

_____

_____

10. Name two other counties. (Use an atlas or a map.)

_____

_____

B ADVERBS

Adverbs add to the meaning of verbs. In the legend, the adverb 'closely' tells us more about the way Glastonbury is connected to King Arthur. The word 'miraculously' tells us more about the way the staff came to life.

'Closely' and 'miraculously' both end 'ly'. That is how most adverbs are formed — by adding 'ly' to an adjective.

Complete these sentences by choosing a suitable adjective from the list below and forming it into an adverb. (Use each adjective only once.)

loud	faint	sad	swift
patient	graceful	sound	quiet
bright	smart	joyous	sudden

1. The racing driver drove past the chequered flag _____

2. The ballet dancer moved across the stage _____

3. The noisy football supporters sang _____

4. The clouds cleared and the sun shone _____

5. We were so tired we all slept _____

6. The soldier marched up to the officer and saluted _____

7. She was very upset and cried _____

8. We did not want to be heard so crept out _____

9. It was a long time ago but I could still remember _____

10. The train was very late but we waited _____

11. The choir sang _____

12. The train stopped _____

C

Read through the following passage and think of words that best fit the spaces.

It may not _____ you to _____ that trees have been important in

myths and _____ for many years _____ over the world, and have

featured strongly _____ religious writings. Groves of _____ in

the forests have been used as tree sanctuaries, as _____ places for

important meetings and _____ ceremonies. People have worshipped

_____ tree spirits, and _____ the trees themselves. Trees have

_____ used as important _____ for religious ideas, bringing

life, knowledge _____ wisdom.

D   Make twenty words from the word 'important'.

1. _____   11. _____

2. _____   12. _____

3. _____   13. _____

4. _____   14. _____

5. _____   15. _____

6. _____   16. _____

7. _____   17. _____

8. _____   18. _____

9. _____   19. _____

10. _____   20. _____

Roman Roads

There is a saying that 'all roads lead to Rome'. This is a brief account of how the saying originated.

The Roman Empire lasted from <u>approximately</u> 290BC to AD410. During that period the Romans <u>established</u> an <u>extensive</u> network of very straight roads to help them conquer and <u>govern</u> their vast territories. The *road* system was carefully <u>designed</u> and <u>constructed</u> to enable the armies of Rome to reach the furthest parts of their Empire in the quickest time possible. They used skilful building and engineering <u>techniques</u> to cross rivers and to pass *through* mountain ranges. At the height of the Empire *there* were in <u>excess</u> of 50,000 miles of first class roads and over 200,000 miles of lesser roads.

In the Forum in Rome there was a Golden Milestone, *right* at the heart of the Empire. The <u>routes</u> leading out from the Forum were measured off at regular distances from this stone, so that soldiers and other travellers on these *great* roads would know exactly how far away from the 'Eternal City' they were. So it was true for hundreds of years that all roads in Europe and Northern Africa at least, really did lead to — or from — Rome.

Although most of these roads <u>deteriorated</u> and fell into disrepair after the decline of the Roman Empire, some of them still <u>exist</u> today. In Italy and other parts of Europe, these ancient roads are still the backbone of the modern road systems. So, as we are driven along motorways in fast cars, we might think of a Roman officer's horse plodding along at the head of a column of Roman soldiers.

A   Answer these questions in sentences.

1.   How many years did the great era of Rome last?

_____

2.   Why did the Romans build the extensive road network?

_____

_____

3. How do you know that the road network was well planned?

_____

_____

4. Which two physical features are mentioned as needing great skill?

_____

_____

5. Where was the Golden Milestone?

_____

_____

6. What was the special significance of the Golden Milestone?

_____

_____

7. What other name is used for Rome in the account?

_____

_____

8. What was true for hundreds of years?

_____

_____

9. Why do you think the Roman roads fell into disrepair when the Empire declined?

_____

_____

10. Can you think of two reasons why Roman roads were built as straight as possible?

_____

_____

B Define these words (they are underlined in the account).
You may use a dictionary if you wish.

1. approximately _____

2. established _____

3. extensive _____

4. designed _____

5. constructed _____

6. techniques _____

7. excess _____

8. routes _____

9. deteriorated _____

10. exist _____

C Homophones are words that sound the same but have different spellings and meanings. In the account, there are five words in italics: *road, through, there, right* and *great*. Write a sentence to show the meaning of each homophone below.

1. road _____

    rode _____

2. through _____

    threw _____

3. there _____

    their _____

4. right _____

    write _____

5. great _____

    grate _____

D CORRECTING ERRORS

One mistake has been made in each sentence below.
Spot the error and write out the sentence correctly.

1. Roman roads were usually bilt straight.

    _____

2. In times of trouble, Roman armies needed to travel quick.

    _____

3. Roman roads was measured from the Golden Milestone.

    _____

4. A mile was the distants covered in 1,000 paces.

    _____

5. Each of the girls have a new book.

    _____

6. I took Jane's ball but mother made me give it back to she.

    _____

7. She grumbled that she never went nowhere.

    _____

8. I think I know who must have took my bike.

    _____

9. The flowers were to expensive for me to buy.

    _____

10. I heard the clatter as the cavalry past my window.

    _____

E POSSESSIVE APOSTROPHE

Towards the end of the account are the words **officer's horse**.
To show that the horse belongs to the officer, we insert an apostrophe (') before the letter s. However, if we were thinking of more than one officer (plural) the apostrophe would come after the officers, e.g. **two officers' horses**.

Insert possessive apostrophes where needed in the following sentences:

1. Bills dog chased Marys pet rabbit.

2. Joans uncle owns a toy shop.

3. Mr Johnsons car is outside the Owens house.

4. The soldiers helmets were made of steel.

5. Three girls work was displayed on the headteachers noticeboard.

6. The goalkeepers jersey was muddy and the captains shirt was torn.

7. The boys leg was broken and his sisters arm was bruised.

8. The artists easel was knocked over by the riders horses.

9. The ships funnel was painted black.

F Make ten words from the word 'administration'.

1. _____   6. _____

2. _____   7. _____

3. _____   8. _____

4. _____   9. _____

5. _____   10. _____

The Weather

The weather affects us all and it is often said that 'the weather' is the main <u>topic</u> of conversation in Britain. This is, perhaps, because our weather <u>changes</u> so quickly and <u>frequently</u>.

Did you know that it is <u>usually</u> warmer in cities than in the countryside? This is because we use fuel to heat our homes and to power our cars and lorries. The burning of fossil fuels in this way <u>creates</u> heat but it also releases carbon dioxide into the atmosphere. Scientists say that this is creating a 'greenhouse effect' which may result in more dry desert <u>areas</u> in the world. There is also a <u>danger</u> that ice at the poles may melt causing the seas to rise and <u>perhaps</u> flooding low-lying cities.

A People who study and forecast the weather are called meteorologists. Like most scientists they frequently use some special words. Use dictionaries, encyclopaedias and/or other reference books to find the meaning of these words:

1. atmosphere _____

2. barometer _____

3. condensation _____

4. dew _____

5. drought _____

6. evaporation _____

7. forecast _____

8. precipitation _____

9. thermometer _____

B Find alternatives for the eight words underlined in the passage. You may use a dictionary or thesaurus if you wish.

1. topic _____   5. creates _____

2. changes _____   6. areas _____

3. frequently _____   7. danger _____

4. usually _____   8. perhaps _____

C Read through the following passage and think of the words that best fit each of the spaces.

Temperature and Thermometer

When we discuss the weather we often talk about how

warm it is. Temperature is measured on a thermometer.

A thermometer has a narrow _____ tube with

a bulb at the bottom. _____ bulb is filled with

fluid, usually mercury _____ alcohol, which

expands as temperatures rise and _____ when

temperatures fall. A scale is printed _____

the base-board of the thermometer so _____

the height of the column of liquid _____

be measured.

Temperature is measured on one _____ two

scales. The Centigrade scale has 0°C _____

the freezing point of water and 100°C _____

the boiling point of water. The other _____ is

Fahrenheit and water freezes at 32°F _____

boils at 212°F.

One of the highest _____ ever

recorded was 134°F (56·7°C) in a place _____

Death Valley in California, one of the _____

was minus 126·9°F (‾88·3°C) in Vostok in Antarctica.

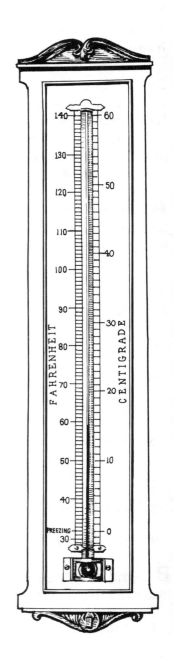

D   TEMPERATURES AROUND THE WORLD

The temperatures at noon in cities around the world are printed in many newspapers. On 10th November 1992 the following temperatures were reported:

	°C	°F
Athens	22	72
Berlin	4	39
Dublin	9	48
London	11	52
Miami	27	81
Rome	20	68
Sydney	26	79
Tokyo	11	52

Answer these questions in sentences.

1.   Which city was the hottest?

   _____

2.   Which city was the coldest?

   _____

3.   What was the difference in degrees Fahrenheit between the hottest and coldest cities?

   _____

4.   Which city had the same temperature as London?

   _____

5. Which country is each city in? Write your answers in sentences.
(If you do not know, look in an atlas.)

_____

_____

_____

_____

_____

_____

_____

_____

E

Write a 'weather word' for each letter of the alphabet.
Be as creative as you can to fill all the gaps.

atmosphere _____   _____   _____

_____   _____   _____

cumulus _____   _____   _____

_____   _____   _____

_____   _____   _____

_____   _____   X-ray lightning

_____   _____   _____

_____   _____   _____

_____   _____

Test 1

A

1. 26	**3.** z	**5.** j	**7.** m	**9.** h
2. d	**4.** u	**6.** s	**8.** t	**10.** f

B

1. Check each word is in alphabetical order and spelt correctly.
2. black, brown, green, pink, purple, red, violet, white, yellow

C

aeroplane, bus, car, fire-engine, helicopter, jeep, lorry
motorcycle, tractor, van

D   Underlined Pairs   *Any three from these possible answers.*
There may be other possibilities.

1.	king	ring	sing thing wing (example given)
2.	fell	well	bell dell sell tell yell
3.	ball	wall	call fall hall small tall
4.	windmill	hill	bill kill mill sill till will
5.	hole	sole	bole dole mole pole vole
6.	hide	inside	bride ride side tide wide
7.	duck	stuck	buck cluck luck muck suck
8.	bake	cake	fake hake rake sake take wake
9.	stile	mile	file pile tile vile while
10.	time	chime	dime lime mime slime

E

1. The lost dog was barking by the gate.
2. The aeroplane zoomed noisily over the house.
3. The kind nurse bandaged my grazed knee.
4. The goldfish swam round and round its bowl.
5. My teacher marked all my sums right.
6. The children in our class are good at painting.
7. A funny clown made the audience laugh.
8. My favourite dinner is chicken and chips.
9. Our cat loves a saucer of milk to drink.
10. Our television set has gone wrong so we cannot watch it.

Test 2

A
1. 6
2. udders
3. 10
4. In summer cows are kept out in fields.
5. Cows are given clean straw to lie on.
6. clean

B   *Specimen answers — wording can be different.*
1. Farmers keep cows because they give milk.
2. Cows are milked twice a day.
3. Cows are milked when their udders are full.
4. In summer cows are kept in fields.
5. In summer cows eat grass.
6. In winter cows are kept in cowsheds.
7. In winter cows eat hay.
8. Cows lie on straw.
9. A baby cow is called a calf.
10. Two other farm animals are a sheep and a pig.
    (or other farm animals)

C
A baby cow is called a calf. A newborn calf lies on the grass beside its mother. The cow licks her calf to clean it. When the calf tries to stand, its legs are wobbly. The calf soon gets hungry. It drinks warm milk from its mother.

D
Check each sentence for sense and correct use of capital letter, full stop and verb.

Test 3

A   *Specimen Answers*
1. There are four verses in the poem.
2. There are four lines in each verse.
3. A child is talking in the poem.
4. The mother is being spoken to.
5. A driving licence is a document that proves you have passed your driving test.
6. a football, a whistle, a bike, a toy, a lorry, a tractor, a bus

B

Specimen Answers

1.	Verse 1a	<u>like</u>	<u>bike</u>	<u>hike</u>	<u>pike</u>
	1b	<u>nag</u>	<u>Jag</u>	<u>bag</u>	<u>rag</u>	<u>stag</u>
	Verse 2a	<u>real</u>	<u>wheel(s)</u>	<u>deal</u>	<u>heel</u>	<u>meal</u>
	2b	<u>car</u>	<u>far</u>	<u>bar</u>	<u>jar</u>	<u>star</u>
	Verse 3a	<u>fuss</u>	<u>bus</u>	<u>puss</u>	<u>truss</u>
	3b	<u>new</u>	<u>through</u>	<u>blue</u>	<u>do</u>	<u>stew</u>
	Verse 4a	<u>old</u>	<u>told</u>	<u>bold</u>	<u>hold</u>	<u>sold</u>
	4b	<u>brain</u>	<u>plane</u>	<u>lane</u>	<u>rain</u>	<u>gain</u>

C

1. I would
2. do not
3. that is
4. you would
5. would not
6. need not
7. I am
8. you will
9. you have
10. what is
11. I have

D

1. can't
2. doesn't
3. he's
4. I'm
5. that's
6. we'll
7. you're
8. they've
9. shouldn't

E

Correct arrangement for *The Ghost's Song* is:

I'm a terrifying ghost,
and I'll scare you for certain.
I'm a cross between a monster
and an old net curtain.

I can walk through a wall,
I can imitate a bat,
I can turn myself bright purple,
and then horrify the cat.

Test 4

A   *Specimen Answers*

1. Daura was a hot, dry place with one well in which a big snake lived.
2. permit means allow
3. Because the snake only allowed them to draw water once a week, the people often went thirsty.
4. A hot/weary/brave prince came from another land.
5. The snake woke when he heard the prince striding to the well.

6. The snake hissed at the prince.

7. & 8. Check for appropriate answers.

B

1. grave, depressing, earnest, alarming, worrying
2. large, huge, gigantic, enormous, colossal
3. fearful, frightened, timid, scared, nervous
4. valiant, courageous, daring, bold, fearless

C

1. terror, fear
2. broad, wide
3. enormous, gigantic
4. halt, stop
5. new, modern

6. feeble, weak
7. foe, enemy
8. dusk, twilight
9. round, circular
10. astonish, surprise

D

Here is the punctuated version of *The Fox and the Stork.*
Check that the underlined parts have been corrected.

<u>A</u> fox invited a stork <u>to</u> dinner, but all he provided <u>were</u> large flat dishes of <u>soup. T</u>he fox lapped his up <u>easily but</u> the stork with her <u>long</u> bill <u>could</u> not get any. The sly fox <u>laughed</u> cruelly at her misfortune.

So, a <u>few</u> days <u>later</u>, the <u>stork</u> returned <u>the</u> invitation. She <u>served</u> a tall <u>narrow</u> jug of food <u>to each</u> of them. <u>With</u> her <u>long</u> thin <u>neck</u> and bill she could reach <u>right</u> to the <u>bottom</u> of her jug<u>.</u> The fox, however, <u>went</u> hungry <u>because</u> he could not reach the food in his jug<u>. I</u>t served him right for <u>playing</u> a trick on the stork<u>.</u>

Test 5

A

1. Long ago in China there lived a man name Ts'ai Lun.
2. Ts'ai Lun found out how to make paper.
3. He put bits of rag, bark, straw, plant stems and old fishing nets in a stone bowl.
4. He beat the ingredients with a wooden mallet.
5. Then he added water and beat the mixture to a pulp.
6. He noticed that the wet bits stuck together and spread out so they floated on the water like a mat.
7. Ts'ai Lun made a sieve to lift out the pulp mat.
8. He left it to dry in the sun.
9. When it was dry, he found he could write on it.
10. That was how the first piece of paper was made.

B

Check each sentence for sense and punctuation.

C

Check if question appropriate, and check for correct
use of question mark.

D

Sentence to dictate.
Read once at normal speed and then again word by word.
Check punctuation and spelling (especially underlined words).

The <u>letter</u> from <u>their teacher arrived before dinner</u> on the
day the <u>children started</u> the <u>holiday</u>.

Test 6

A
1. Underline: invite, stay, is, are, is, have, fish, hope,
   accept, write, tell, enjoy, make, give
2. Underlined altogether (18)

B

1.	began	6.	flew	11.	fell	16.	caught
2.	ate	7.	gave	12.	met	17.	paid
3.	left	8.	knew	13.	went	18.	rode
4.	blew	9.	was	14.	lost	19.	sold
5.	dug	10.	built	15.	heard	20.	sang

C

Sentences to dictate.
Read once at normal speed and then again word by word.
Check punctuation and spelling (especially underlined words).

The <u>famous five could</u> not wait to get down from the dinner
<u>table.</u> If the <u>message</u> was <u>right</u> there was <u>going</u> to be some
<u>action</u>. They did not want to be <u>late.</u>

D

Check the letter for:
Heading Setting out of address and date
Conclusion Setting out of final message and signature
Content Relevance, interest, spelling and punctuation

Test 7

A *There are other acceptable synonyms.*

1.	live	4.	build	7.	like
2.	protect	5.	collect	8.	send
3.	crowds	6.	kinds	9.	assistance
				10.	enemy

B

Caterpillars, leaves, fungi, seeds, sweet things

C *Specimen Answers*

1. Ants use smells to send messages to say where food is.
2. They use another smell to ask for help with carrying something heavy.
3. They use their sense of smell to detect enemies.

D

Honeydew is a fluid obtained from greenfly.

E

1. looking after babies
2. searching for food
3. cleaning the nest
4. protecting the nest

F

	ANTS	BEES
How they live (SIMILAR)	1. live in large groups 2. the queens lay all the eggs 3. they build the nests 4. they can communicate 5. the workers collect food 6. the workers care for the babies	
What they eat (DIFFERENT)	caterpillars, leaves fungi, seeds	nectar, pollen honey
How they keep food (DIFFERENT)	they keep greenfly to milk	they store spare honey and pollen in wax cells
How they communicate (DIFFERENT)	by sense of smell	by dancing

Test 8

A
1. Merlin
2. A sword
3. The Lady of the Lake

Specimen Answers
4. The sheath was more valuable than the sword because the person wearing it would lose no blood if they were wounded.
5. When Arthur took the sword the arm slowly submerged into the water.
6. We know Arthur felt more confident about dealing with his enemies because the last sentence tells us he felt more capable of fighting them.

B *Accept these words or other appropriate ones.*
1. politely, considerately, graciously, respectfully
2. pointed out, showed
3. seized, gripped, held
4. sunk, lowered
5. cover, case
6. injured, hurt

C Eleven sets of speech marks.

D
Arthur thought it was time he got married. He summoned Merlin and said, "I want to marry a princess called Guinevere." Merlin was a wizard and knew it was not a good idea. He advised Arthur not to marry Guinevere. Arthur said, "I want no one but Guinevere for my wife so go and arrange the wedding."

E
Anne left her house late so she ran as fast as she could to catch the bus. The bus was early but she still caught it because the driver waited for her. Anne was grateful to the driver so she thanked him.

F
1. I	3. him	5. her, she	7. me, they
2. me	4. She, me	6. We, them	8. His, he, us

G

1. disagree
2. uncertain
3. uncomfortable
4. unemployed
5. dislike
6. dismount
7. unequal
8. dishonest
9. uneven
10. unexpected
11. disadvantage
12. undress
13. unfair
14. disrespect
15. disloyal
16. unwary
17. disappear
18. unfortunate
19. disappoint
20. disbelieve
21. disallow
22. unwrap
23. unusual
24. disobey
25. unhealthy
26. untidy
27. unpack
28. disapprove
29. unhappy
30. disqualify
31. unknown
32. distrust

H

1. subway
2. interval
3. postpone
4. submarine
5. incomplete
6. prepare
7. illegal
8. rewrite

I

1. lovable
2. famous
3. careless
4. waitress
5. princess
6. comfortable
7. gosling
8. wonderful

Test 9

A *Specimen answers — there are other possibilities.*
1. A steam engine works by heating water to make steam and using the pressure of steam to work machinery.
2. Electricity is produced in power stations.
3. Wood is a renewable resource because it comes from trees and new ones can be planted.
4. A geologist is a person who studies the earth's crust and investigates rocks and minerals.

B *There are other possibly acceptable words.*
1. strength or force
2. obtainable
3. found
4. made
5. finally
6. share or part

C

1.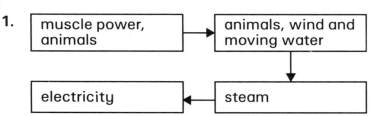

60

2. *Specimen Answers*

   toaster, washing machine, fridge, hairdryer, iron

D

1. fox	6. bat	11. snow
2. tortoise	7. pig	12. daisy
3. lion	8. owl	13. grass
4. peacock	9. mule	14. ice
5. bee	10. berry	

E

1. . . . sandwiches, cakes, biscuits and ice cream.
2. . . . hens, sheep, cows, pigs and horses.
3. . . . sums, reading and writing.
4. . . . travel, sport and giants.
5. . . . tea, sugar, rice, bread and butter.
6. . . . herring and cod.
7. . . . 8, 15, 19 and 20.
8. . . . a new bike, a computer game and an annual.
9. . . . three brothers, one sister, two aunts and three uncles.

F

Passage for dictation. Read through once at normal speed
and then again word by word. Include the title in the test.
Check punctuation and spelling (especially underlined words).

Power for Transport

Bicycles depend on the muscle power of humans.
Cars and lorries are fuelled by petrol or diesel.
Boats are driven by oars, sails or fuel.
Modern trains have diesel or electric engines.

Test 10

A *Specimen answers. Check meaning is clear.*

1. A legend is a story which has been handed down through
    the ages and is often thought to be historical, although there
    is no evidence.
2. The Glastonbury Thorn was a hawthorn tree.
3. The first one was planted when Joseph of Arimathea
    drove his staff into the ground.

4. Joseph of Arimathea was a rich man who lent his tomb
    to the disciples for the burial of Jesus.
5. In front of the Parish Church of St John the Baptist.
6. Every year blossom from the tree is sent to the
    Royal Family.
7. Originally the tree blossomed on Christmas Eve.
8. It now blooms on a day in January because the British
    calendar was altered in 1752.
9. The thorn can be seen in the county of Somerset.
10. Two other counties are Lancashire and Cumbria. (*Or other counties.*)

B
1. swiftly
2. gracefully
3. loudly
4. brightly
5. soundly
6. smartly
7. sadly
8. quietly
9. faintly
10. patiently
11. joyously
12. suddenly

C surprise hear legends all in trees
special religious the even been symbols and

D *Specimen answers — there are more words.*
map, man, mat, main, train, ant, port, part, trap, rat,
imp, pin, rain, pain, pint, print, pant, ram, ran, pan

Test 11
A, B and C have specimen answers — there are other possibilities.
A
1. The great era of Rome lasted about 700 years.
2. They built the road network so they could move about their
    Empire speedily.
3. We know the road network was well planned because the
    account says the system was carefully designed and constructed.
4. The account says that skilful techniques were needed
    to cross rivers and pass through mountains.
5. The Golden Milestone was in the Forum in Rome.
6. The Golden Milestone was the starting point for measuring
    distances from Rome.
7. Rome is also called the 'Eternal City'.
8. That all roads led to - or from - Rome.
9. There was nobody to keep the roads in good repair.
10. The roads were built straight because a straight road is shorter
    than a curved one and has no bends for enemies to hide behind.

B

1. approximately   roughly, about
2. established   set up
3. extensive   wide ranging
4. designed   planned
5. constructed   built
6. techniques   special methods
7. excess   greater than
8. routes   roads to be followed
9. deteriorated   got worse
10. exist   are in being

C

1. road   The road system was carefully designed.
   rode   The emperor rode on a white horse.
2. through   The road passed through mountains.
   threw   The horse reared up and threw the rider.
3. there   In the Forum there was a Golden Milestone.
   their   Soldiers obey their officers.
4. right   We hope we have the right answers.
   write   We have to write our answers.
5. great   The Roman Empire was a great empire.
   grate   We burn coal and logs in the grate.

D

1. bilt = built
2. quick = quickly
3. was = were
4. distants = distance
5. have = has
6. she = her
7. nowhere = anywhere
8. took = taken
9. to expensive = too expensive
10. past = passed

E

1. Bill's   Mary's
2. Joan's
3. Johnson's   Owens'
4. soldiers'
5. girls'   headteacher's
6. goalkeeper's   captain's
7. boy's   sister's
8. artist's   riders'
9. ship's

F *Specimen Answers*

station, nation, dim, drain, mad, man, tin, nod, mind, not

Test 12

A *Specimen Answers*
1. the mixture of gases surrounding the earth
2. an instrument for measuring air pressure
3. water formed as vapour cools
4. tiny drops of water forming on the ground
5. a long time without rain
6. when heat turns water into vapour
7. to predict what the weather will be
8. when rain forms in the clouds and falls
9. an instrument for measuring temperature

B *Specimen Answers*
1. subject
2. alters, varies
3. often
4. generally, normally
5. makes, causes, generates
6. regions
7. fear, risk
8. maybe, possibly

C

| glass | The | or | contracts | along | that | can | of |
| as | as | scale | and | temperatures | called | lowest | |

D
1. Miami was the hottest city.
2. Berlin was the coldest city.
3. The difference in degrees Fahrenheit between the hottest and coldest cities was 42°F.
4. Tokyo had the same temperature as London.
5. Athens is in Greece.
   Berlin is in Germany.
   Dublin is in Eire.
   London is in England.
   Miami is in the USA.
   Rome is in Italy.
   Sydney is in Australia.
   Tokyo is in Japan.

E *Specimen Answers (invent if necessary, e.g. X-ray lightning)*
atmosphere, blizzard, cumulus, drizzle, eclipse, freezing, gale, hurricane, isobar, Jack Frost, khamsin, lightning, monsoon, nimbus, overcast, precipitation, quarter-wind, rain, showers, thunder, umbra, vane, windy, X-ray lightning, yellow snow, zonda